Twig the Fairy

and the

Mermaid Misadventure

by Kathy Gfeller & Linda Clayton

Photographs by Grant Brummett, LunahZon Photography and Bobby Vyne
Design by Linda Clayton

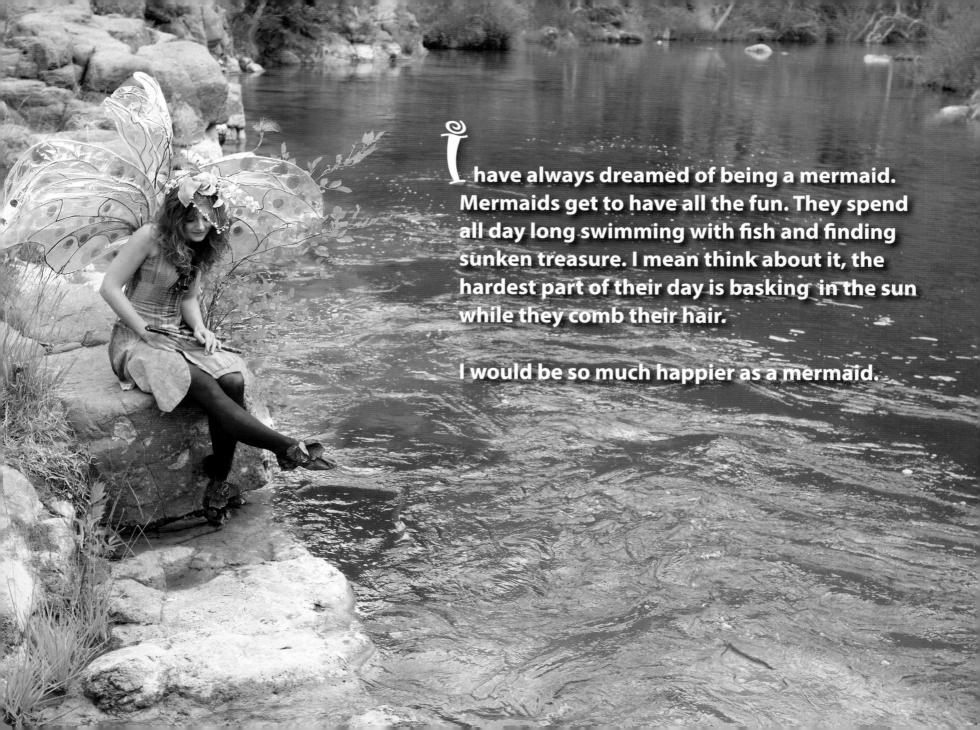

I have always dreamed of being a mermaid. Mermaids get to have all the fun. They spend all day long swimming with fish and finding sunken treasure. I mean think about it, the hardest part of their day is basking in the sun while they comb their hair.

I would be so much happier as a mermaid.

My friend Coral just doesn't understand how lucky she is.

She thinks her beautiful tail is slimy and gross and that life as a fairy would be so much more fun.

She whispered that if I truly believed in something with all of my heart, anything was possible.

That night something totally weird happened.

Weird, and ...

Awesome!

finally got my wish.

Swimming with fish is even better than I imagined.

This mermaid thing is so easy.

I'm heading out to deeper water.

Ewwwww!

Seaweed.

My thoughts about mermaids basking in the sun while combing their hair were wrong.

It's not so much basking as it is combing. It takes hours to get seaweed out of your long locks. Hours, and hours and hours and hours and hours and ...

This is Not how I imagined this.

Finally..

...seaweed free.

O pen sea, here I come.

Look!

other mermaids!

played my most beautiful fairy greeting

but they just laughed,

looked at me funny,

and started to swim away

I wonder how mermaids talk to each other? It's obviously not the same as fairies.

Awkward.

This must be how mermaids dance.

Look at the time! It's four o'clock, I can't wait to have tea.

Or not. Turns out, you can't pour tea underwater.

This is *So Not* what I imagined.

I was feeling out of sorts without my tea, and I was discombobulated. I had fun with the other mermaids but I also missed flying with my friend Zinnia, so I went to my favorite waterfall to watch the sunset.

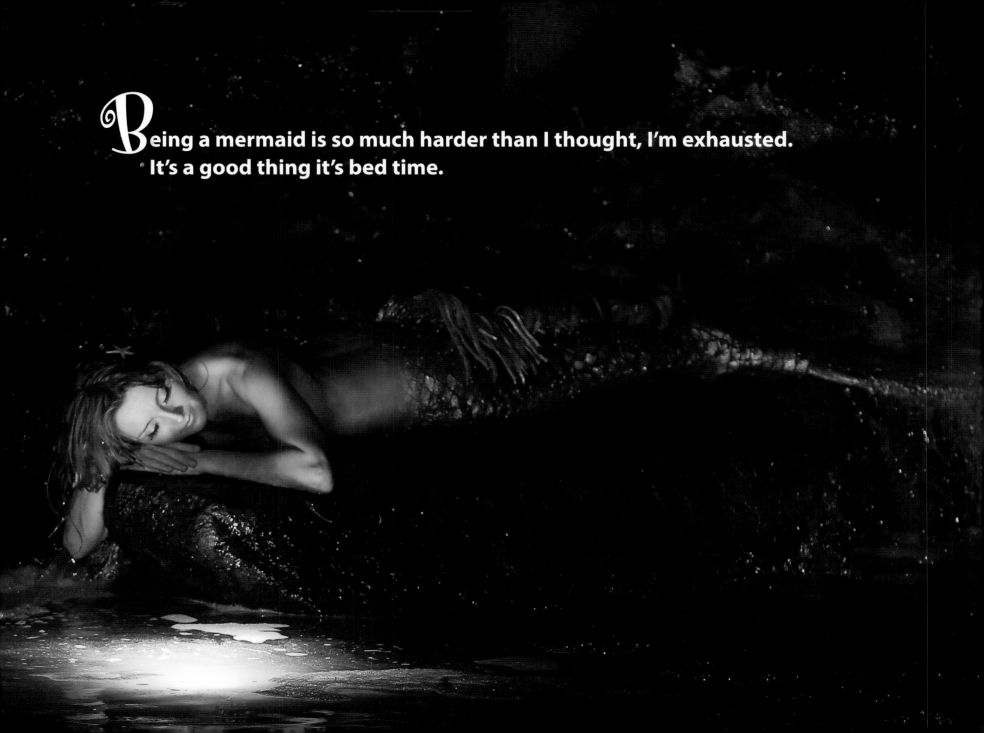

Being a mermaid is so much harder than I thought, I'm exhausted. It's a good thing it's bed time.

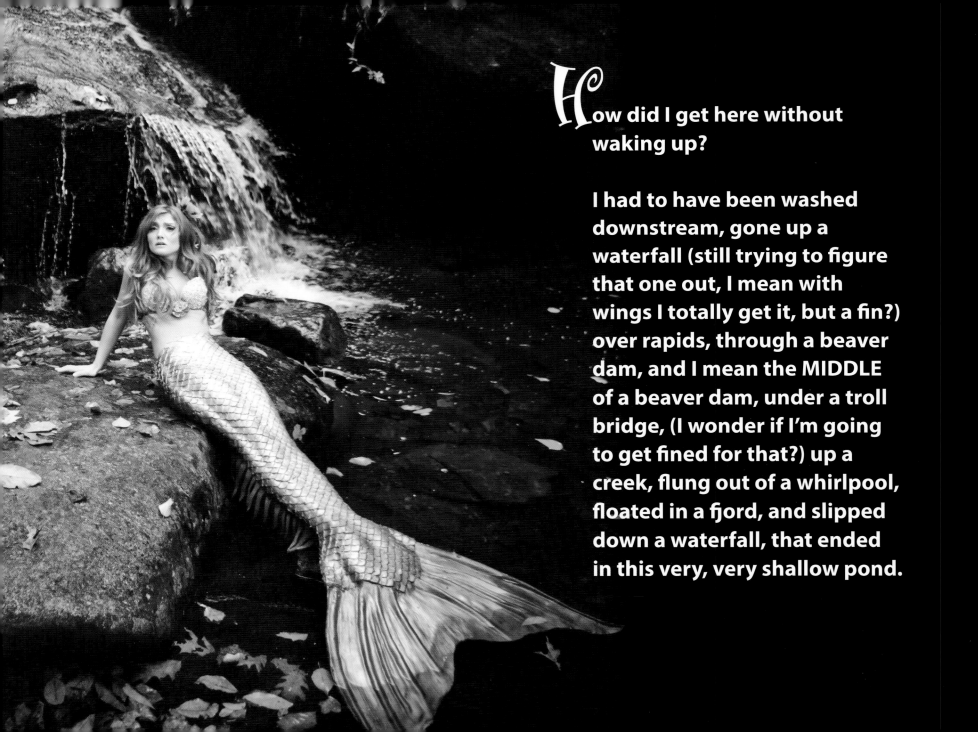

How did I get here without waking up?

I had to have been washed downstream, gone up a waterfall (still trying to figure that one out, I mean with wings I totally get it, but a fin?) over rapids, through a beaver dam, and I mean the MIDDLE of a beaver dam, under a troll bridge, (I wonder if I'm going to get fined for that?) up a creek, flung out of a whirlpool, floated in a fjord, and slipped down a waterfall, that ended in this very, very shallow pond.

I think I'm really stuck. Maybe this mermaid thing isn't that easy afterall.

This is *Really Not* what I imagined.

My best friend Zinnia the Fairy always shows up just when I need her most.

Fairies are just as amazing as mermaids. She blew a bubble big enough to carry me back to deeper water.

I found Coral as fast as I could. She told me about a couple of crash landings and a terrible wing incident which we will never speak of again. We quickly agreed it would be best for trees, fish and all of fairy kind if we switched back to who we really are.

As I fluttered my wings and she flopped her tail we both breathed a big sigh of relief. I learned a huge lesson. Life is so much harder when you're trying to be someone else. I've never been so happy to be *exactly* the way I am.

La Fin

(The End)

Twig
the Fairy

Executive Glitter Producers:

Will Oatman   Russell Tavares   Natalie Cramer
Ron Tencati   Heather Von St James   Mackenzie Koll
   Photography   Ryan Opel   Jordan Davis
Jim Cassidy   Colin D. Henry   Green Goddess
Rachel Lubich   Jeff Lewis   Grange, NJ

Special thanks to:

Moon Mermaid, Christine Mermaid, Heather Trevino, Zinnia the Fairy, Allie Causin,
Anna Von Winter, Jessica Nigri, Monica Brumment, Michelle Hardy, and John Behr

Glitterrific Producers:

Grant Brummett
Green Goddess Grange
Jason DeMars
Jordan Fields
Kieran McKiel
Cheryl Ammeter
Eldy Stefanou
Mark Sholund
Harold Elias-Perciful
Wayne Abbott
Kaitlynn McAulay
Gillian Hayes
Becky Bodine
Bruce Henry
Bennett Liestman
The Fae Guardian
Anna Meisner
Hope and Wes
Joanne Chi Lee
Ajshe's Angels
Michael Dixon
Mystyne-Marie Grant
Richard Snell
Alexandra Concordia

Chad-Michael Simon
Marvin Bechtold
Trevor Dwire
Emma Grace Calvert
Abigail Hope Calvert
Ochen Kaylan
Joe and Deborah Burke
Matt Swords
Crystal Johnston
Rachel Maslow
Chris Dulabone
Brittnee and Brooke Anderson
Yolaine Baca Robinson
Bill Woehr
D. Chris Davis
T. Greyfox
Kate, Luke & Will Friese
Matthew P. Christensen
Patrick Storfer
Bedorah
Salem Reynolds
Sylvia Stoehr
The Higgins-Williams family
Ella Ebner-Clayton

Jonea & Frankie Behr
John T. Hodge
Patrick McDowell
Olórin
Michael The Red
Evelyn Schock and Atticus Strand
Rachel VanDyne
Cecilia Hawks
Samantha Andrew
Brian "Bean" Leonardo
Lady Cricket Loheac Whitwood
Kovo Mendoza
Katrina Marie Wicks
Greg Hasse
Dorinda Bazanele
Helen Pine
Karol Kurtz
Joe "BakeySmurf" Hendrickson
Justin Block
Calvin Letson
Jennifer Leibler
Angela Suzanne Sands
The Mueller Family
Steffi (Shaylee) Main